CLASSIC LANDFORMS OF THE

# NORTH DEVON COAST

This guide is dedicated to my parents, in
gratitude for a natural North Devon childhood.

*Peter Keene*

CLASSIC LANDFORMS OF THE

# NORTH DEVON COAST

PETER KEENE
**Senior lecturer in Geography,
Oxford Brookes University**

*Series editors*
Rodney Castleden and Christopher Green

Published by the Geographical Association
in conjunction with the
British Geomorphological Research Group

THE GEOGRAPHICAL ASSOCIATION

# PREFACE

Some elements in the landscape we see around us are very ancient; some change very rapidly, almost while we watch. Landscape scientists (geomorphologists) can explain these landforms, and the processes that make them, but much of their work is published in specialist journals and is therefore not available to the general public. It is one of the aims of this series to make up-to-date explanations of the most striking and interesting landforms in England and Wales accessible to all. These classic landforms are naturally of interest to geography students, both in school and university, and we hope that the style and format of this series of guides will make them easy to use both at home and in the field. We hope that a clearer understanding of the origins and dynamics of landform development through time and space will help both student and visitor to maximise their appreciation and enjoyment of the landscape.

Encouraged by the response to the first edition of the Classic Landform Guides we are pleased to introduce this new edition, enhanced by colour photographs, new illustrations and with the valuable addition of 1:50 000 map extracts by kind permission of the Education Team, Ordnance Survey. The relevant maps for the area covered in this book are Ordnance Survey 1:50 000 Landranger sheets 180 and 190; please refer to the current Ordnance Survey Index for 1:25 000 availability.

**Rodney Castleden** *Roedean School, Brighton*
**Christopher Green** *Royal Holloway, University of London*

ISBN 1 899085 18 1
This edition first published 1996
Published by the Geographical Association, 343 Fulwood Road, Sheffield S10 3BF
The views expressed in this publication are those of the author and do not necessari
represent those of the Geographical Association.
The Geographical Association is a registered charity no. 313129
*Cover photograph:* The shore platform at Welcombe Mouth *Photo:* Peter Keene
*Frontispiece:* Castle Rock *Photo:* Peter Keene

# CONTENTS

## Safety

The coastal cliffs should be approached with care. The cliff edges are often crumbly, overhanging and covered with dense turf. The tidal range is high (8m), and cliff-foot walks should not be attempted with an incoming tide.

**Acknowledgements**

The Geographical Association would like to thank the following organisations for permission to reproduce material in this publication:
Nicholas Horne Ltd, for the picture on page 8;
Cambridge University Collection of Air Photographs, for the picture on page 18;
erofilms Ltd, for pictures on pages 25 and 43; English Nature, for picture on page 30;
ir William Halcrow and Partners, for the wave orthogonal material used in Figure 10.
Mapping reproduced from Ordnance Survey 1:50 000 Landranger mapping with the permission of The Controller of Her Majesty's Stationery Office
©Crown Copyright 82324M 09/96
*Copy editing:* Sue Martin
*Illustrations:* Paul Coles
*Series design concept:* Quarto Design, Huddersfield
*Design and typesetting:* Armitage Typo/Graphics, Huddersfield
*Printed and bound in Hong Kong by:* Colorcraft Limited

# INTRODUCTION

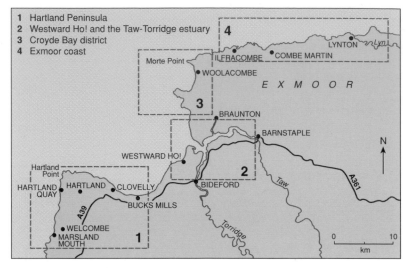

1 Hartland Peninsula
2 Westward Ho! and the Taw-Torridge estuary
3 Croyde Bay district
4 Exmoor coast

*Figure 1: The areas studied in the context of the North Devon coast. The relevant Ordnance Survey 1:50 000 maps are sheets 180 and 190; please refer to the current Ordnance Survey index for 1:25 000 coverage.*

## Geological background

The rocks of North Devon were deposited in a large sea basin, the northern limb of which alternated in Devonian times between land and shallow water, leading to the deposition of sediments which were later to become the coarse sandstones, shales, limestone, mudstones and slates of Exmoor. In Carboniferous times sedimentation continued and, as part of the **Variscan Orogeny,** the basin was deformed into a long trough (synclinorium) trending east-west which at times may have been brackish rather than fully marine. These earth movements initiated a series of major thrusts and folds, the products of which are so magnificently demonstrated in the coastal cliffs of North Devon.

The main axis of the synclinorium lay to the south of this district so North Devon represents only the northern limb of this basin, rocks of increasing age being exposed in sequence as one moves northwards (Table 1). Close to the central axis of the basin, for example south of Embury Beacon (SS 216195), the folds exhibited in the cliffs are predominantly upright, but as one travels north the principal folding becomes more inclined, until on the western coast of Exmoor the folds are strongly overturned to the north. These major folds may have a wavelength of between two and ten kilometres. The scale of the more minor folds varies considerably, and in part depends upon the coherence and internal strength of the beds within which the folds were formed. The mudstones and shales tend to have many small folds,

# Table 1: Geological formations of the North Devon Coast: a chronological table

| Name and age (MYBP) | North Devon member | Nature of rock |
|---|---|---|
| QUATERNARY (2) | Detailed on Table 2 | |
| TERTIARY<br>MESOZOIC (230) | Absent except for Eocene granite of Lundy | |
| PALAEOZOIC<br>Permian (280) | Peppercombe outlier | Red sandstone and breccia |
| Culmination of Variscan Orogeny (All rocks older than this heavily folded and faulted) | | |
| Carboniferous | Bude Formation | Massive sandstone beds interbedded with thin sheets of siltstone, mudstone and shales. |
| | Bideford Formation | Cyclic sequences of dark shales, siltstone, mudstones and sandstones formed in conditions similiar to shallow deltas. |
| (350) | Crackington Formation | Rapidly alternating beds of sandstone and dark to black mudstones and shales. |
| Devonian | Pilton Shales | Shales with siltstone, sandstones and limestones. |
| | Baggy Sandstone | Sandstones, shales and siltstones. |
| | Upcott Slates | Massive sandstones pass upwards into grey-green and purple slates. Very steep dip 55-66° |
| | Pickwell Down Sandstone | Fine-grained grey-green and purple-red sandstones. Thin beds of shale. |
| | Morte Slates | Smooth grey-green and grey-purple slates. Infrequent beds of limestone and fine-grained sandstones. |
| | Ilfracombe Slates | Slates. Thin limestones and occasional sandstones. |
| | Hangman Sandstones (Grits) | Coarse sandstones with some mudstones. |
| (395) | Lynton Slates | Thinly bedded well-jointed fine-grained slates and sandstones. (Lynton Beds). |

sometimes with a wavelength of only a few metres; whilst the tougher sandstones can have folds of a wavelength of several hundred metres.

These folded cliffs and shore platforms are cut by many faults trending north-west to south-east, often with subordinate faults crossing north-east to south-west. Most faults show a displacement of only a few metres, but some have a throw of over 200m. The two largest, the still-active Sticklepath and Lustleigh faults, cross both the county of Devon and the Bristol Channel, and have caused displacements of several kilometres. At Portledge (SS 384246), close to where the Sticklepath and Lustleigh faults cross the Devon coast, an east-west trending fault helps to preserve a small outlier of Permian red sandstone, the only example in the district. From the sea it is a sharp splash of colour against the sombre Carboniferous sandstones and shales.

# HARTLAND PENINSULA

## Coastal plateaux

It is likely that you will approach the Hartland Peninsula on the A39, following the watershed between the gentle, shallow, inland-draining tributaries of the River Torridge, and the short, steep-sided coombes that notch the coastline. This land of windswept woods was enclosed with thick earth-banked hedges long before the days of the turnpikes, and the roads zigzag about the boundaries of these old fields, giving the sensation of anything but flatness. Yet as the horizon will confirm, the landscape is dominated by remarkably gentle surfaces (see Photo 1). The region is characterised by a staircase-like arrangement of largely unwarped plateaux. It is a sobering thought for anyone seeking explanation of landforms in the area to consider how little is known of the origin of these large-scale features.

On the plateaux themselves there is no sign of the intense folding

**Photo 1: The coastal plateau, above Hartland Point,** *planes the intensely folded beds of the Bude Formation; to the right of the lighthouse is a fault-controlled landslip, Blagdon Cliff (SS 229274) Photo: Nicholas Horne Ltd*

**Photo 2: Warren Cliff, Hartland Quay** *(SS 226249). The zigzag chevron folds of the Crackington Formation are truncated by a coastal plateau, here at 85m OD*
*Photo: Peter Keene*

previously described. The land surface truncates the underlying rocks with little regard for their resistance or arrangement. Nowhere is this more apparent than where plateau meets cliff top, as at Warren Cliff, Hartland Quay (SS 226249) (see Photo 2). Clearly these are erosional surfaces, but the exact mechanism by which they were cut is not clear. Classically, these plateaux have been interpreted as each being directly related to a past sea level, carved either by marine planation or by terrestrial processes gradually reducing the land to an erosional plane close to sea level. Thus the staircase of plateaux could be related to sea levels, perceived to be falling gradually, with pauses, throughout the **Neogene** and **Pleistocene.**

Evidence now suggests that at least the higher surfaces in south-west England were fashioned by subaerial processes, the same processes that are wearing down the landscape today, and that these surfaces may have been unrelated to the sea levels of the time. Some plateaux may be very ancient features subsequently buried beneath sedimentary rock and only exhumed in the comparatively recent geological past.

The extensive surfaces that survive on the watersheds are not level, so it is misleading to be very specific about their heights. However, the highest surface in the district swells to between 200 and 210m OD, whilst other surfaces clearly recognisable in the landscape are 130-155m and 75-90m.

# The cliffs

The coastal footpath from Hartland Point (SS 230278) southwards to Marsland Mouth (SS 212174) and on into Cornwall is one of the finest cliff walks in Britain. Steep cliffs, often fresh-faced and near vertical as at Hartland Quay (Photo 2), expose tightly-folded interbedded Carboniferous fine-grained sandstone and shales (Table 1). The axes of these folds are predominantly east-west, following the Variscan trend, and here running at right angles to the coast. The shore platform exposes the stumps of cliffs already removed by marine action, slicing across the structures in a horizontal plane. (The cover photograph of Welcombe Mouth (SS 212179) demonstrates this discordance clearly.) Where shales and sandstones are interbedded, as at Welcombe, the rocks have been differentially eroded, the shales being removed relatively rapidly, leaving limbs of upstanding sandstone. More massive beds of sandstone run seawards in a series of jagged reefs which still take a toll on shipping along this coast. In the cliff faces, slanting caves are excavated in weaker shales and mudstones or where the sea has exploited faults or zones of weakness along the axial planes of folds (Photo 2).

### Process control

Near-vertical cliffs have only short-term stability. Over a period of time subaerial (land) processes, in particular those associated with the penetration of water into joints and bedding planes, will cause cliff failures. Were these the only sets of processes involved, then rock failures and other subaerial slope processes would degrade these cliffs comparatively rapidly, reducing slope angles initially to between 26° and 34°. The steep cliffs of the Hartland coast are only maintained by wave-attack actively eroding the cliff foot, precipitating cliff collapse by the removal of basal support.

The west coast of the peninsula directly faces the storm environment of the Atlantic, the direction from which the most powerful and most damaging waves will come, the dominant wave direction. This is also the direction from which winds most frequently blow; the prevailing wind direction. These factors combine to make the coast a high wave-energy environment, with frequent strong on-shore winds pushing steep, short wave-length storm waves towards the shore. In such an environment debris supplied to the beach by cliff falls is rapidly removed, exposing the cliff foot to renewed wave attack. The slope base is undercut, causing further mass failure of overlying rocks. Thus the cliff retreats maintaining a steep fresh-faced wall. In such an environment even a 'hard rock' coast such as this may be retreating 2-4cm a year. It is an unforgettable experience to stand on the clifftops above Hartland Quay in the full fury of an Atlantic storm, and then drive the short distance to the other side of the peninsula to experience the calm of Clovelly (SS 318248) or Buck's Mills (SS 356237).

If you compare Photos 2 and 3 you will see that this startling contrast is also reflected in the cliff scenery. The north-east side of the

***Photo 3: Cliffs at Keivill's Wood.*** *The bulging cliff is the foot-slope of a large rotational slip being reactivated by marine attack at its toe Photo: Peter Keene*

peninsula faces away from the Atlantic storms and although the waves from these storms are refracted (bent) round Hartland Point, they fail to penetrate this corner of Bideford Bay very effectively. The most powerful waves on this side of the peninsula come from the north and north-east, a direction which provides only a short **fetch** and from which winds blow less frequently. The prevailing wind here is off-shore; this is therefore a lower wave-energy environment. Undercutting of the cliffs is less effective and removal of cliff-foot debris slower. In the absence of vigorous wave attack the **shore platform** is not well developed. On this coast the balance has seemingly shifted in favour of subaerial processes, which here have been given time to make their mark. Cliff scars identify the sites of old and active landslips. The debris fans on the foreshore are sorted slowly by the waves, but boulders – the **lag deposit** – remain for many years. At Keivill's Wood (SS 352237) (Photo 3) near Buck's Mills, a large curved cliff scar (a rotational slip) is sited immediately above a pronounced coastal feature known as the 'Gore' (350240). This large, flat boulder spit, exposed for 500m out to sea at low tide, has been interpreted as the lag deposit of an exceptionally large but unrecorded landslip or debris slide, its shape substantially modified by subsequent wave action. If this is the case, then this is an ancient feature, for it is marked on navigation charts of 1795.

A small area of larger boulders is to be found on the foreshore between the Gore and the cliffs (SS 350238). At first sight this may look like the remains of a secondary landslip but in fact these roughly shaped boulders are the foundations of a small quay constructed here at the start of the seventeenth century.

The survival of the extensive pebble beds which make up the Gore may be related to its low wave-energy location favouring the accumulation of pebbles and boulders in this corner of Bideford Bay.

### Geological control

The relative importance of marine and land processes as factors controlling cliff shape (morphology) have been discussed. To this must be added the strength and structure of the rocks making up the cliffs. In the absence of quantitative data we can only make qualitative judgements. It is useful to consider where on the triangular grid provided (Figure 2) a particular cliff element under study might be placed. Locations along the horizontal axis of the graph have been considered. Now let us consider the vertical axis.

It is clear that the local arrangement of rock beds, faults and zones of weakness will have a considerable effect upon the shape of the cliff at any particular location, but let us apply this more generally, comparing the two sides of the Hartland peninsula. The features most commonly associated with cliff modification by subaerial processes are coastal landslips. Figure 6 demonstrates that the landslips correlate far more closely with the outcrop of a particular rock type than with location on the more sheltered side of the peninsula. Despite

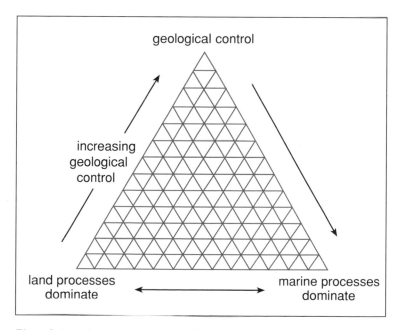

**Figure 2:** *Some factors controlling cliff shape*

some massive sandstone bedding, the Bude Formation (Table 1) seems particularly susceptible to slope failures, perhaps due to the incompetence of shale beds which separate the tougher sandstone sheets.

A second important geological factor is the trend of the Variscan fold structures across the peninsula. The axes of these folds are approximately east-west. On the west coast this orientation produces structures that run straight out into the sea, one example of which is the shore platform at Welcombe Mouth (see cover photograph). On other parts of the peninsula, between Hartland Point (SS 229279) and Blackchurch Rock (SS 299267) and between Clovelly (SS 318248) and Peppercombe (SS 380243), the axes of the folds run nearly parallel to the coast. In these locations the limbs of the folds therefore tend to be directed either towards or away from the sea. Those sections of the cliff where the limbs dip south, away from the sea, will be particularly susceptible to 'toppling' failure (Figure 3). The sea undermines the supporting rock causing beds to topple outwards. A mantle of coarse scree is created under a comparatively steep upper cliff.

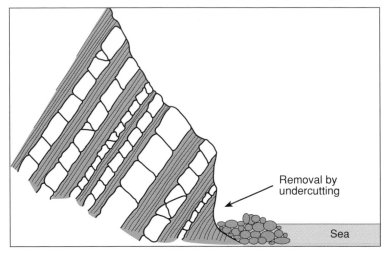

*Figure 3:* A site susceptible to toppling failure

A common feature on these stretches of coast is a series of low, grassy hollows running parallel to the cliff edge. These are tension cracks signalling future failures. Figure 6 shows a close relationship between cliff failures and coasts with an east-west orientation. The shape of cliffs is often the result of a complex relationship among a variety of processes and geological structures.

## The coombes

One of the pleasures of walking the coastal footpath is to drop periodically into the sheltered coombes which deeply incise the plateau edge. The long profiles of these valleys have been truncated by cliff retreat. In the larger coombes this has encouraged the sharp incision of the streams in their lower courses, often ending in a tumbling descent to the beach. The Abbey River (SS 226256) joins the sea in this fashion cutting a short 'canyon', with a waterfall at its head. The rock floor of the Abbey River grades to a sea level lower than the present one but of unknown date. Smaller and less vigorously incised streams, similarly truncated by coastal retreat, terminate in coastal hanging valleys. Occasionally, as at Windbury Head (SS 292266), they have high waterfalls spilling directly into the sea.

Three coombes of particular interest are:

- Abbey River, best seen near its mouth at Blackpool Mill (SS 226256), and accessible from Berry (SS 234254) or Hartland Quay (SS 222246) (Figure 6)

- Strawberry Water, best seen at Welcombe Mouth (SS 212180). A short dirt-track leads down the valley to a clifftop car park

- Marsland Water, best seen at Marsland Mouth (SS 212174) and accessible by walking from Mead Corner (SS 222176).

These coombes display evidence of major environmental changes which have considerably modified the coast. These modifications are related to a series of extreme climatic fluctuations which characterise the Quaternary (see Table 2, page 40). At least three major phases can be readily identified in all these valleys. The Marsland valley serves as an example.

**Phase 1** The first recognisable stage in the evolution of the valley is the deep incision of the coombe into the plateau edge. In cross-section the valley has a flat rock-floor flanked on either side by bedrock slopes with long rectilinear sections standing at angles between 26° and 34°.

**Phase 2** The rock-cut valley is partly infilled with an unconsolidated mass of angular stones embedded within a matrix, or background, of finer-grained material, the whole being derived entirely from rocks found locally. In Figure 4a the infill is assumed originally to have filled the valley to line A-B-C. Although some 15m thick in places, this material exhibits little to suggest that conditions changed very much during the period of its accumulation. The unconsolidated infill was the product of processes active during the last (Devensian) glaciation, when the region experienced Arctic, **periglacial** conditions. At that time, some 18 000 years ago, sea levels were about 110m below those of today. About 70km away to the north across a dry Bristol Channel the foot of the vast ice-sheet, which covered much of Wales at the peak of the Devensian, would have been visible.

This was a phase when the production of hillside rock debris was accelerated by **frost-action** and the transport of this debris downslope by **solifluction** clearly outstripped the ability of the summer stream to remove or sort it. Under these conditions the valley became choked with the debris, locally known as **head.** Head is common throughout North Devon but is most easily recognised in the coombes or in hill-foot situations, where it accumulated to considerable depths. It seems likely that the rectilinear nature of the bedrock slopes flanking the valley was also largely the product of these conditions.

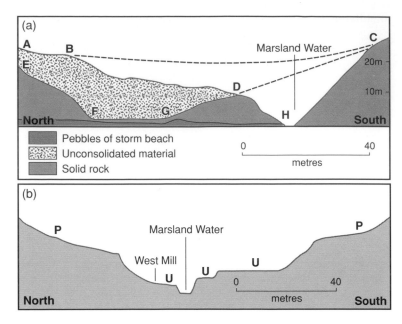

*Figure 4: Cross-sections of the Marsland valley (see text for explanation of letters)*

**Phase 3** In the post-Devensian climatic amelioration, frost-action and solifluction decreased, so that the load provided to the stream diminished to the point where, far from being choked with debris, the stream had enough spare energy to renew active erosion. The reactivated, downcutting stream carved a series of meander terraces as it incised itself into the head deposits.

These terraces (marked U in Figure 4b) are unpaired and have curved, abandoned meander bluffs. They are particularly well developed at West Mill (SS 215175). Nearer the stream mouth (SS 212174) is a fine, abandoned meander terrace, complete with a raised meander core. On the valley side is a more steeply sloping terrace which is the surface remnant of the original valley solifluction infill (P in Figure 4b).

The Marsland Water stream eventually eroded a trench through the head infill and reincised itself into bedrock. Being superimposed from above, the location of this incision was arbitrary. At the valley mouth (Figure 4a), the stream has cut a small rock gorge on the southern side of the valley (B-D-H-C), whilst the original valley (E-F-G-D) remains choked with debris. The same sequence occurred at Welcombe Mouth except that here the abandoned valley lies to the south of the present stream. In both cases good valley cross-profiles, conveniently cut by the encroaching sea, can be viewed from the beach.

The local valley networks include sections running parallel to the coastline. At Speke's Mill Mouth (SS 226235) coastal recession has breached the outer wall of one such coombe (Figure 5a), beheading the lower valley (Photo 4). At the point of capture, the Milford Water is still 48m above sea level, and the stream plunges to the beach in a series of fine, structurally controlled waterfalls. The gentle and regular long profile of the sea-dissected (now abandoned) lower course of the stream can be followed northwards, behind St Catherine's Tor (SS 225242) (Photo 5), as far as Hartland Quay, where the hotel itself occupies the former valley floor (Figure 5b).

Typical of local coombes, these dry remnants have flat, rock-cut floors with steep valley sides containing long rectilinear sections at angles between 28° and 34° (Photo 4). Unlike the coombe already described, the Milford Water, with its sea-dissected continuation, has only a thin skin of head on its floor.

A good cross-section of the valley floor can be seen from the lowest car park at Hartland Quay (SS 223247), looking south. The tributary valleys of the larger coombes are much more markedly V-shaped and lack the flat rock floor. An example of this is the Wargery Water (SS 228240), a former tributary to the Milford Water. Its plan suggests strong structural control.

The lack of valley floor debris and the similarity in shape between the coastal continuation of the Milford Water Coombe and known meltwater channels in west Wales has prompted the suggestion that this sea-dissected valley, and a smaller example at Smoothlands (SS 226264), may have been modified by ice-margin meltwaters.

*Photo 4: **A sea-dissected valley** viewed from above Speke's Mill Mouth looking north. The rectilinear slopes silhouetted by shadows stand between 32° and 34°*
*Photo: Peter Keene*

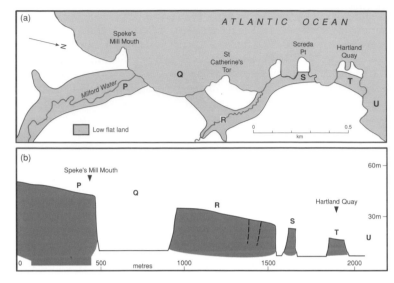

**Figure 5:** *Coastal coombes to the south of Hartland Quay – (a) map and (b) cross-section*

**Photo 5: St Catherine's Tor** *and shore platform at low tide*
*Photo: Cambridge University Collection of Air Photographs*

Although this coast was glacier-free during the Devensian, **tills**, or associated deposits, at Fremington (SS 529315) and in the Scilly Isles, suggest that an earlier glaciation brought an ice-cap to the north coast of Devon and Cornwall. The most likely candidate for this is the Anglian glaciation of some 450 000 years ago. In such a situation, it has been argued, meltwaters may well have been trapped between land rising to the south-east and the thick ice-cap rising away to the north-west over what is today the Bristol Channel. Such meltwaters could have escaped by pouring along what is now the coast, between land and ice, utilising and modifying any convenient route, for example T-S-R in Figure 5a.

This suggestion remains highly speculative through lack of evidence. One stumbling block is that the immediate 'inland' portion of the Milford Water Coombe, south of P in Figure 5a, exhibits the same flat-floored steep-sided characteristics as the supposed meltwater section. However, there remain intriguing anomalies related to the valley. It narrows to the north (the direction of flow) and the valley sides have some odd breaks of slope including the one seen on the hillside opposite St Catherine's Tor (Photo 5).

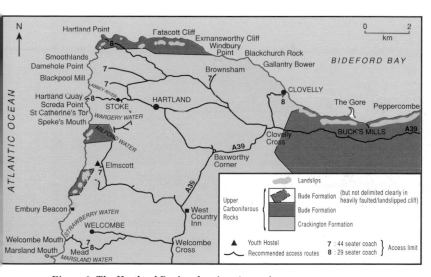

*Figure 6: The Hartland Peninsula – location and access map*

## Access

The easiest access to the most spectacular sites on the west coast is from Hartland Quay where even large coaches can reach the upper clifftop car park (SS 225247). Routes to other coastal locations mentioned in the text are labelled in Figure 6, although access to some coastal sites is sometimes difficult for large vehicles. Advice on accessibility may be obtained from Heard's Coaches, tel Bideford (01237) 473534.

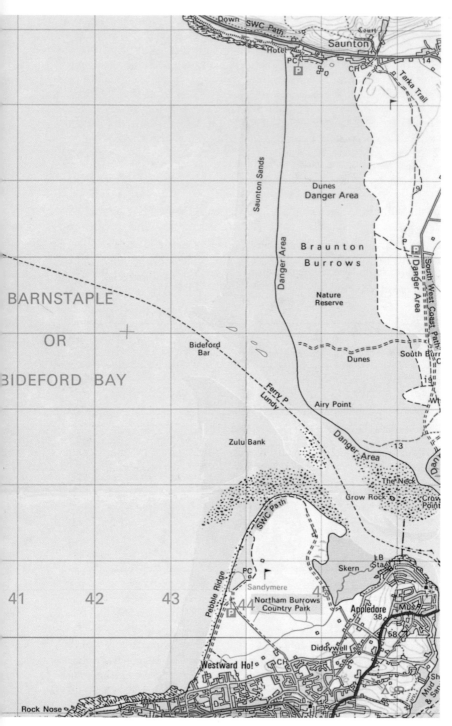

# WESTWARD HO!

Westward Ho! is a useful centre easily reached from the A39 trunk road and surrounded by examples of classic coastal scenery – not least, its cliffs.

## Long-term coastal change: the cliffs

The cliffs of the Hartland Peninsula have been considered as a function of present land and marine processes and the local geology. The cliffs of the Westward Ho! district demonstrate the importance of including in any such assessment relict forms surviving from former climatic conditions which favoured rather different environmental relationships.

Sea levels during the last interglacial (Ipswichian, see Table 2, page 40) were a few metres higher than today's, cutting marine cliffs which in general matched the position of the present coastline. The fall in sea level brought about by the subsequent Devensian glacial stage left these former cliffs well above the sea, and subject to the same periglacial processes as those affecting the coombes previously discussed. Cliffs were degraded, producing bed-rock slopes with long rectilinear sections at angles of between 27° and 32°. Scree and head material accumulated at the cliff foot, spilling out onto the former sea floor. With the ending of the coldest stage of the Devensian, sea levels returned to near interglacial levels – rising some 100m between 18 000 and 6000 years ago, after which the sea rose only slowly. The last 3000 years have seen little sea level change, and to varying degrees the old degraded cliff-forms have been reactivated by the return of the sea.

Figure 7 summarises this activity, and Figure 8 relates the sequence in Figure 7 to the cliffs of Westward Ho! West of Mermaid's Pool (SS 418290) the degraded periglacial rock-slope having been partly removed by postglacial marine activity and the cliffs are typically bevelled: stage 3(c) in Figure 7. For stage 3(d), we would need to travel to a higher wave-energy environment such as Hartland Quay (Photo 2). Landwards of Mermaid's Pool the interglacial cliff (Kipling Tors SS 425289) swings eastwards, its foot increasingly protected by postglacial deposition at the head of Bideford Bay – a good demonstration of stages 3(b) and 3(a). The best location for viewing this sequence is the National Trust footpath which contours Kipling Tors (SS 426289) and which leads to the old coastguard look-out (SS 419279) marked Q in Figure 8. From Kipling Tors the former

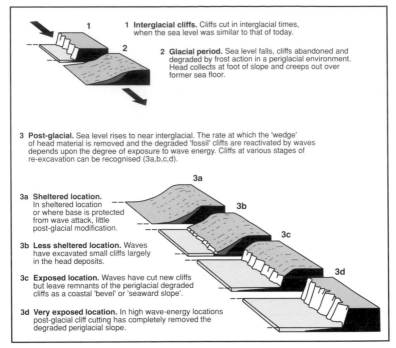

1 **Interglacial cliffs.** Cliffs cut in interglacial times, when the sea level was similar to that of today.

2 **Glacial period.** Sea level falls, cliffs abandoned and degraded by frost action in a periglacial environment. Head collects at foot of slope and creeps out over former sea floor.

3 **Post-glacial.** Sea level rises to near interglacial. The rate at which the 'wedge' of head material is removed and the degraded 'fossil' cliffs are reactivated by waves depends upon the degree of exposure to wave energy. Cliffs at various stages of re-excavation can be recognised (3a,b,c,d).

3a **Sheltered location.** In sheltered location or where base is protected from wave attack, little post-glacial modification.

3b **Less sheltered location.** Waves have excavated small cliffs largely in the head deposits.

3c **Exposed location.** Waves have cut new cliffs but leave remnants of the periglacial degraded cliffs as a coastal 'bevel' or 'seaward slope'.

3d **Very exposed location.** In high wave-energy locations post-glacial cliff cutting has completely removed the degraded periglacial slope.

*Figure 7: Evolution of cliffs in South West Britain*

cliff-line can be followed by eye, or on the map (Figure 11) east to Northam (SS 445292) and then north-east to Appledore (SS 459306), passing landwards of the postglacial depositional feature of Northam Burrows (Photo 6). On the far side of the Taw-Torridge estuary the abandoned cliff-line can be picked up on the landward side of Braunton Burrows and traced to where it meets the sea at Saunton Down (SS 445380), a mirror image of Kipling Tors. From the coastguard lookout Q (SS 419289) or from the old railway cutting on the coastal path R (SS 419290) in Figure 8, the coastline west to Hartland Point can be viewed. Below, at low tide, the wide shore platform displays folding, fine wrench faults exploited by straight gullies, and differential weathering and erosion emphasising the ridges of pale sandstone which cross the shore platform. The fault-displacements in these sandstone beds are very clear.

These sandstone ridges and intervening low-lying areas of shale and siltstones form part of the Bideford Formation. These rocks have characteristics suggesting cyclic deltaic sedimentation. Deltas typically become shallower over time, sediments getting coarser until sands are deposited. Periodically the accumulation of deposits causes subsidence so that the cycle is repeated, starting again with the finest silts.

Between Mermaid's Pool (SS 418290) and Cornborough (SS 411280) folding has displayed the beds of the Bideford Formation 'end on', so that a series of nine such cycles, each identifiable by a sandstone ridge, can be recognised on the shore platform. The first

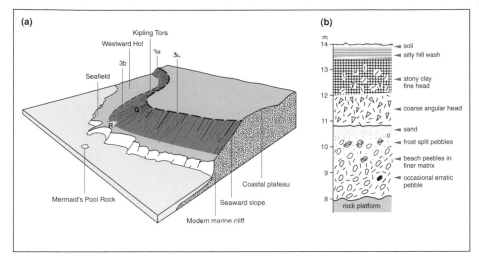

*Figure 8: (a) block diagram of coastal cliffs at Westward Ho! (b) cliff section at Seafield*

(oldest) cycle, clearly reflected in shore platform morphology, lies immediately below our viewpoint, and runs from the Mermaid's Pool Sandstone (SS 418290) to the Rock Nose Sandstone (SS 416288) For closer examination a cliff-foot walk from Westward Ho! to Cornborough (SS 411280), where the coastal path is at beach level, can easily be accomplished between tides. Return on the cliff path which follows the line of the old railway, dismantled in 1917.

The shore platform exposed at low tide along this stretch is up to 300m wide. The time available for the sea to cut this platform in the postglacial period of present day sea levels is probably 3000 years, implying an average sea-cliff retreat of 10cm/year. Even if this were a very high wave-energy environment such as the Hartland coast, where a rate of 2-4cm/year has been suggested, the platform seems too wide to have been cut entirely in postglacial times.

Seafield Meadow (SS 422291) is part of the coastal solifluction apron, absent west of Mermaid's Pool. The apron is composed of upper layers of head overlying soliflucted pebble beds assumed to be part of the Ipswichian beach which fringed the foot of Kipling Tors (Figure 8). These deposits are best examined in the cliff face at SS 422291, approached by walking over the storm beach westwards from near the Patio Pool (SS 426292). The **raised beach** rests on a raised shore platform, at this point at about +8m OD. Look eastwards (back towards Westward Ho!) and this raised shore platform and accompanying raised beach appear to decrease visibly in height, but in fact the modern cliff cuts diagonally across the old raised platform so that the modern cliff is progressively further from the former cliff base. Still further east, at a site now obscured by the modern sea-wall (SS 432293), the raised pebble beds, overlain by head, were reported to be 3m above present high tide level.

The sequence proposed in Figure 7 adequately explains most of

23

what we observe, but may be regarded as simplistic in that such sequences have occurred repeatedly during the Quaternary. Furthermore there is evidence that at least in the later part of the Quaternary, sea levels revisited and modified the same shorelines several times. The forms we see may therefore be the results of several such episodes, and this may help to explain the unaccountably wide shore platforms noted.

The only evidence we have of this at Westward Ho! is the occurrence of a suite of shore platforms near to the present sea level. Below the +8m OD platforms at Seafield (SS 422291) the crests of low sandstone stacks have been suggested as possible remnants of a platform at +5m OD. The main wave-washed platform associated with modern sea levels is at 2-3m OD, but this is terminated seawards by a 2m cliff which has an even lower platform at -1.5m OD (SS 424926) at its foot. This lower platform, exposed at low tide, is similar in level to the modern sandy beach.

These long-term coastal changes are the result of climatically determined events such as glaciations causing sea level oscillations and slower tectonic (earth) movements.

## Medium-term coastal change: the Pebble Ridge

Cliff-falls to the west of Westward Ho! provide debris for a coarse storm beach which fringes the cliff-foot continuously from Clovelly to Westward Ho! The shales and mudstones are rapidly reduced to material fine enough to be lifted by waves and lost to the beach system. Sandstone beds, often failing along iron-stained joints, fall to the beach as large angular orange-brown blocks, but these become rounded and polished into hard grey pebbles which travel eastwards by littoral drift. At Westward Ho! the supply of fresh cliff material ceases but fine sandstone cobbles continue along the foreshore as a pebble ridge flanking Northam Burrows for some 3km and accumulating in a recurving spit at the estuary mouth (Photo 6).

The Pebble Ridge is a comparatively recent feature and has been subject to considerable modification at least over the past 150 years. Navigation charts of 1847 and detailed estate maps of 1855 and 1861 show the ridge as being 1.8km long, extending approximately to X on Photo 6. The position of the ridge has been reliably documented only since the foundation of Westward Ho! as a Victorian seaside resort in 1864. Since that date the crest of the Pebble Ridge has been pushed landwards by up to 150m (Figure 9). In the 1870s erosion at Westward Ho! forced the hasty dismantling and re-erection – some way inland – of several only recently completed, buildings. The former position of one such building, the Union Club, is shown in Figure 9.

The uneven growth of the Pebble Ridge and the fact that its crest has been periodically pushed landwards is probably related to fluctuations in the rate of supply of pebbles from the west. There may be some cyclic pulsing of pebbles along the cliff foot, rather as cusps of

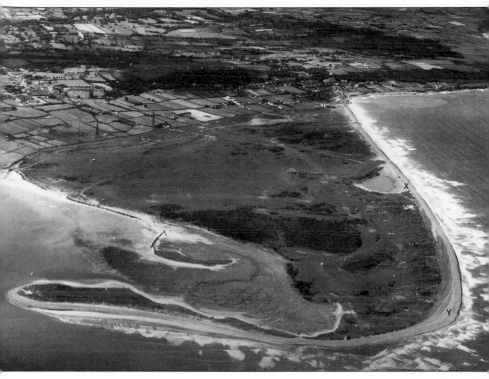

***Photo 6: Northam Burrows and Westward Ho!***
*Pebble Ridge, 1947. For explanation of X and Y see text. Photo: Aerofilms Ltd.*

material (ords) move southwards along the Holderness coast. Supply may be related to variations in landslip frequency along the coast between Westward Ho! and Clovelly.

The height of the ridge has certainly decreased in recent years. It is estimated that the net loss of pebbles along this stretch between 1886 and 1974 was 100 000m², representing a rate of net loss of about 1200m² per year. The local council has initiated a scheme of beach replenishment and is currently moving pebbles from the distal end of the ridge to the slipway end at Westward Ho! (SS 433294) at a rate of 15 000m² per year. The air photo (Photo 6) was taken in 1947. At that time the north-eastern section of the ridge, location Y on Photo 6, showed evidence of accretion. Several low lichen-covered ridges lay inside the storm ridge and it is estimated that the 1947 ridge lay some 25m seawards of its 1886 position. However, changes in the river mouth sand and shingle banks seem increasingly to have focused incoming waves on this section of the Pebble Ridge. Figure 11 includes a computer printout which predicts how high tide storm waves, here of 5 second **wave-period** arriving from the north-west, are refracted by river-mouth shoals to focus their energy on the northern corner of the ridge, location Y (SS 445319). Between 1959 and 1996 the crest of the ridge here has retreated by 30m. In 1978

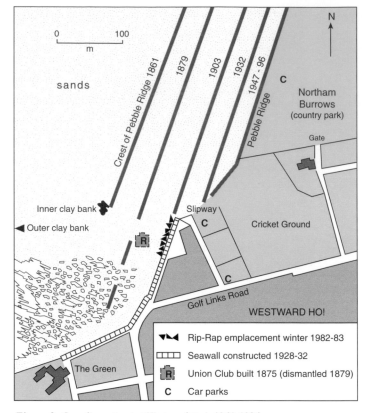

**Figure 9:** *Coastline retreat at Westward Ho!, 1861-1996*

rock armour was emplaced to reinforce the corner of the ridge most susceptible to wave attack, but with only partial success.

### Access

Access points to this area are shown in Figure 11. The slipway car park (SS 433294) provides access to the southern end of the Pebble Ridge. Northam Burrows is a Country Park. A car park at Sandy Mere (SS 438306), approached through gates at SS 445298 or SS 435295, gives good access to the northern end of the Pebble Ridge where sand dune (SS 440310) and salt marsh (SS 451312) sequences can also be examined. Northam Burrows Country Park Visitor Centre, Northam Burrows, Northam, Bideford, tel Bideford (01237) 479708 (SS 441309) has a useful local display and educational service.

## Short-term coastal change: the beach

We accept wide, sandy beaches as part of the West Country north coast scene, yet should wonder at the survival of these sediments in such a hostile environment. Beaches are built in such a way that they naturally dissipate the energy of the waves which break on them. The interaction between waves and beach constantly modifies the shape of the beach, causing it to adopt a form which will absorb the energy of the incoming waves as efficiently and evenly as possible. Beach systems which do this inefficiently do not survive.

The energy of the wave is proportional to the square of its height ($H^2$). The rate at which this energy arrives on the beach is related to the wave period (T). The energy of the wave is therefore a function of both its height and its speed ($E \alpha H^2T$). Wave energy is dissipated principally by the turbulence of the breaking wave and by the waves agitating and lifting the beach sand particles. In a high wave-energy environment, one with steep, high-frequency 'storm' waves, a wide beach of gentle gradient can, if there is enough sand to go round, spread the task of absorbing wave energy thinly over a large surface area. Material is combed from the upper beach and deposited in the zone below low water level creating a long, low-angled profile. Lower energy, flat low frequency waves, on the other hand, demand no such response and push material shorewards, allowing a steeper beach profile to develop. The relationship between wave energy and beach profile, given a particular sand grain size, is shown in Figure 10.

Westward Ho! beach demonstrates this ability to adjust rapidly to changes in wave energy conditions. Photo 7 shows a typical summer scene; the sand was found to be 1.2m deep at this point. Each winter sand moves seawards, reflecting the increased frequency of Atlantic storms. Photo 8 was taken during the stormy winter of 1983-84 when exceptional 'adjustments' reached the point where the upper beach ran out of sand, exposing a thick bed of head which, under periglacial conditions, must have spread out at least this far from the degraded cliff-line seen behind. This would have been stage 2 in Figure 7. The modern view approximates to stage 3(a). To the relief of the local

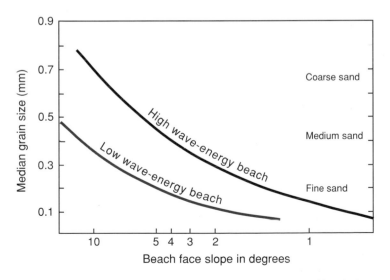

*Figure 10:* The relationship between wave energy, sand grain size and beach slope

**Photo 7: Westward Ho! beach in summer.** *The sand here was found to be 1.2m deep. The rock armour emplacement can be seen at the top of the beach. Photos: Peter Keene*

**Photo 8: Westward Ho! beach during the winter of 1983-84** *is denuded of sand, exposing a platform of clay, and head derived from the 'fossil' cliff-line seen behind Westward Ho!*

holiday industry, the sand returned as usual with the lower energy conditions of spring. Such changes can take place in a matter of days.

A 'healthy' beach, able to adjust in this way, is probably the best form of coastal defence there is. The least efficient energy absorbing structure is a vertical face. Westward Ho! sea-wall, completed in the 1930s, is a good example of such a structure. My childhood was spent in a cottage behind this sea-wall. During winter storms my mother would remove the crockery from the mantelpiece as the cottage reverberated from the wave-energy transmitted directly through the ground from the sea-wall 70m away.

A wave 4m high with a wave-period of 8 seconds arrives on 1km of coast with the power of thirty-two 33-tonne lorries travelling at 110 kph (70 mph). In a 24-hour day that is the equivalent of 345 600 lorries! Small wonder that the sea-wall needed constant remedial work, both for direct damage to the sea-wall itself and for the scour produced by reflected waves meeting incoming combers (clapotis), thus effectively doubling their height ($E \alpha H^2 T$).

Eventually, in 1982-83, rock armour or rip-rap (large individual blocks of rock weighing up to 15 tonnes each), were placed at the foot of the wall to help dissipate the full impact of breaking waves at high tide. The extent of this defence can be seen in Photos 7 and 8.

# THE TAW-TORRIDGE ESTUARY

The estuary is dominated by Braunton Burrows to the north and Northam Burrows to the south. These are largely the product of the postglacial rise in sea level, the Flandrian transgression. During times of low sea level, both the Taw and Torridge were entrenched into bedrock, producing a channel which at Appledore Pool (SS 465312) is 24m below present sea level. The long profile of this rock-floored channel sloped gently seawards, grading to a sea level estimated to be 45m below present sea level and some 12km off-shore. This correlates well with a submerged cliff-line, indicating a still-stand for some time at that level.

*Photo 9: Crow Point in the Taw-Torridge estuary from 2500 feet. In March 1983 its eroded neck, tenously linking it to Braunton Burrows, emphasises the dynamic nature of the estuary environment. Photo: English Nature*

The Burrows on either side of the buried channel are underlain by a rock-platform at about -10m OD. The rising postglacial seas drowned the platforms, depositing estuarine clays and then accumulations of marine sand. Bideford Bay, facing the predominantly on-shore winds, became a vast sediment trap.

## Braunton Burrows

The greatest accumulation of sand has taken place at Braunton Burrows, resulting in a dune system which covers some 1000ha and is one of the largest in the country. Predominantly on-shore winds feed the system with calcareous sand blown from the wide Saunton Sands beach, sections of which dry out at low tide. The dunes form three or four irregular ranks of north-south ridges, alternating with discontinuous low-lying areas (slacks). Fore-dunes cresting at 5m grow immediately behind the beach but are rapidly superseded by large mobile dunes which migrate inland until stabilised by vegetation. The partly stabilised dunes form the highest ridge, reaching over 30m in places, e.g. Flagpole Hill (SS 455352) (see Figure 11).

Active wind-eroded hollows (blow-outs) occur in all the main dune ridges, and towards the east they have initiated parabolic dunes. Low-lying slacks reach the water-table which within the dune complex is dome-shaped, being 6m higher in the central area than on the periphery. A good example of such a slack is Horsebreaker's Slack (SS 452347). It is bounded on the seaward side by mobile dunes which are steadily encroaching upon the low-lying amphitheatre.

A transect from Saunton Sands beach to the Sandy Lane car park (SS 463350) will encompass all the landforms classically associated with coastal dune sequences, together with the typical succession of vegetation so closely related to their development.

### Access

Access to the Sandy Lane car park is easiest from the B3231, Braunton to Saunton road (SS 469374). A second car park situated at Broad Sands (SS 465326) serves the southern part of Braunton Burrows and the estuary mouth. This can be reached by using a toll road through Braunton Marsh past Marstage Farm (SS 484352).

Most of the dunes are leased by English Nature and are a National Nature Reserve. For further details of the reserve contact the Warden, Broadeford Farm, Heddon Mill, near Braunton, North Devon EX33 2NQ, tel 01271 812552.

## Fremington Clay

This site, although not spectacular, is of special interest since it is the only clear evidence that suggests that an ice sheet reached mainland Devon and Cornwall. The possibility that ice reached this far corner of Bideford Bay, perhaps some 450 000 years ago (in Anglian times), has to be considered when interpreting coastal features displaying undated elements inherited from the past.

The sequence of deposits (see right) is best demonstrated at Brannam's Claypit (SS 529317). It includes 6m of pure clay sandwiched between two thinner layers of till or glacially derived deposits. The clay has been interpreted as being a lake-floor deposit, perhaps the result of ice damming the lower reaches of the River Taw. Both tills and clay contain **erratics**, some similar in composition to those found at Saunton and Croyde.

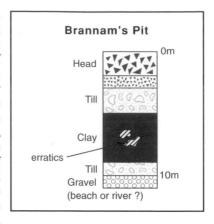

Brannam's Pit is worked for potter's clay and permission to view must be sought from C. H. Brannam (Pottery) Ltd, Roundswell Industrial Estate, Barnstaple, North Devon EX31 3NJ. The clay in the pit can be treacherously soft. Access by road is from the B3233 onto the B3232 800m south of Bickington (SS 531325).

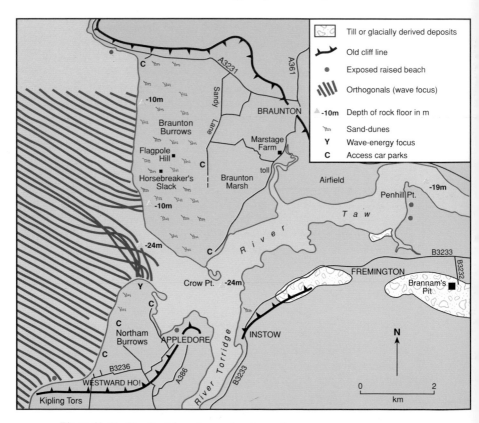

***Figure 11:*** *The Taw-Torridge estuary – location and access*

# CROYDE BAY

## Geological control

The Devonian rocks of the Croyde Bay district (Figure 12) trend west-north-west to east-south-east. Here, on the northern flank of the Devon synclinorium, the major folds are overturned or thrust to the north. Unlike the closely interbedded Carboniferous rocks to the south, these Devonian beds occur in much broader masses, sandstones and shales each dominating alternate stretches of coast. Figures 12a and b demonstrate a close relationship between the plan of the coast and the coastal exposure of rocks of contrasting characteristics. The Baggy Sandstone and Upcott Slates correlate closely with Baggy Point, as do the Morte Slates with Morte Point. Similarly, the Pickwell Sandstones match the broad re-entrant of Morte Bay.

One might be forgiven for simply concluding that this demonstrates the ability of marine processes to erode the coast selectively, the bays representing outcrops which are particularly susceptible to marine attack. The ability of the sea to exploit zones of weakness has already been dramatically demonstrated on a smaller scale along the Hartland coast. This might well be a large-scale example of differential erosion. But whatever may have happened in the past it is not reflected in present-day processes. Even a cursory glance at the Ordnance Survey map will indicate that marine processes are actively cutting cliffs on the headlands, whilst both Morte and Croyde Bays are infilled with wide, low-profiled, sandy beaches, typical of this high wave-energy environment. The beaches are backed by sand-dunes abutting against slopes which are clearly not undergoing marine modification today. However, the story might be rather different if the sands trapped in these embayments were not so abundant.

Another approach might be to consider the differential erosion as principally the result of subaerial processes. As with marine processes, these might be expected to be more active in less resistant beds of rock, so that valleys might be guided along these zones of weakness. If that were the case, these coastal indentations could be interpreted as the result of the landscape being drowned as sea levels rose at the end of the last ice age, during the Flandrian transgression, each bay being an incipient **ria**. However, this interpretation also has its problems. The land immediately behind Morte Bay rises steeply to match the highest land in the immediate district. Indeed, the Pickwell Down Sandstone, despite its coastal exposure coinciding with a bay,

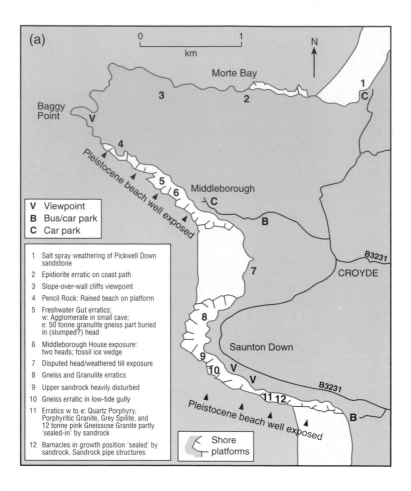

(a)

V  Viewpoint
B  Bus/car park
C  Car park

1  Salt spray weathering of Pickwell Down sandstone
2  Epidiorite erratic on coast path
3  Slope-over-wall cliffs viewpoint
4  Pencil Rock: Raised beach on platform
5  Freshwater Gut erratics;
   w: Agglomerate in small cave;
   e: 50 tonne granulite gneiss part buried in (slumped?) head
6  Middleborough House exposure:
   two heads; fossil ice wedge
7  Disputed head/weathered till exposure
8  Gneiss and Granulite erratics
9  Upper sandrock heavily disturbed
10  Gneiss erratic in low-tide gully
11  Erratics w to e: Quartz Porphyry,
    Porphyritic Granite, Grey Spilite, and
    12 tonne pink Gneissose Granite partly 'sealed-in' by sandrock
12  Barnacles in growth position 'sealed' by sandrock. Sandrock pipe structures

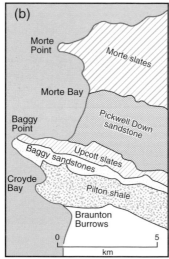

(b)

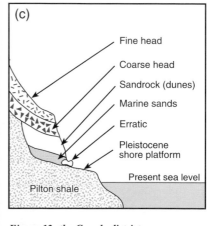

(c)
Fine head
Coarse head
Sandrock (dunes)
Marine sands
Erratic
Pleistocene shore platform
Present sea level
Pilton shale

**Figure 12: the Croyde district**
*(a) location and access, (b) geology and*
*(c) diagrammatic section: Saunton Down*

is regarded as the toughest rock of the district. It is also somewhat anomalous that the weaker Morte Slates occupy a headland. Morte Slates also occur at the southern tip of Lundy Island, but extending the trend-line west-north-west from Morte Point completely misses this exposure, hinting at displacement by faults. It has been suggested that a major fault trending north-north-east lies offshore in line with Westward Ho! and Morte Point. Such a fault perhaps might go some way towards explaining these anomalies.

## Pleistocene inheritance

In common with most British coastlines, the North Devon coast has inherited distinctive features associated with the climatic vicissitudes of the Quaternary. The cliffs on the northern flank of Baggy Point (see Figure 12b and Photo 10) are cut in Upcott Slates. An interglacial cliff, degraded during episodes of periglacial climate and low sea level, has been partly reactivated by the returning sea of post-glacial times. The scene shown fits snugly into the sequence illustrated in Figure 7. However, Figure 2 should remind us that the form of most cliffs is a function of several factors. Here, it is noteworthy that the shoreline runs nearly parallel to the strike of the Upcott Slates (110°), and as can be seen from the stacks in the foreground of the photograph, these slates dip steeply into the cliff (55°-60°). Such relationships have commonly been advanced to suggest structural control of the hog's-back cliffs of the Exmoor coast. Along the northern side of Baggy Point the failure of weaker beds of shale has caused substantial chunks of the cliff to sag seawards as coherent masses. The grassy scars of these sagging failures are visible on the clifftops.

*Photo 10: Slope-over-wall cliffs cut in Upcott Slates* on the northern flank of Baggy Point. Photo: Peter Keene

Pleistocene erratics

High on the crest of these same cliffs (+80m OD) sits a large isolated 500kg block of epidiorite (SS 435407), a basic igneous rock, possibly of Scottish origin. If natural agents are responsible for emplacing this erratic block, it points directly to ice having overridden these cliffs, perhaps the same ice that deposited the Fremington till.

This is by no means the only far-travelled boulder in the district; a whole series has been identified on the coast between Freshwater Gut on the north side of Baggy Point (SS 427400) and Saunton Sands (SS 445377). These boulders vary in composition (Figure 12a), but most imply a northern origin. There is general agreement that they are glacial in origin, although their mode of transport is disputed. Unlike the Baggy Point epidiorite, these erratics are littoral in location, sitting on the shore platforms close to present sea level, prompting the suggestion that they arrived on, or within, grounding icebergs calved from ice-fronts lying to the north or west.

One objection to this theory is the fact that glacial periods associated with such ice advances are also periods of low sea levels. There is plenty of evidence to suggest that at least in the later Quaternary these low 'glacial' sea levels were matched by 'interglacial' sea levels which each roughly attained the present world-wide levels, thus periodically revisiting and reworking the same shorelines, the 'yo-yo' principle shown in Figure 13b.

However, if the 'staircase' of coastal plateaux, so evident in North Devon, is regarded as being related to former sea levels in the Pleistocene, then the sea might be seen as gradually falling, in relation to the land, over a long period. In such circumstances early Pleistocence low 'glacial' sea levels might match those of present interglacials (Figure 13a), making the iceberg hypothesis tenable. Alternatively, a cold start to a glacial might send icebergs south while sea levels were still high. A diversion of the cold East Greenland current southwards, displacing the warm North Atlantic current, might, even within an interglacial, direct icebergs bearing New World erratics onto the shores of South West England. Or then again approaching ice-fronts might depress the crust sufficiently to produce locally 'high' sea levels.

Another suggestion is that the erratics are the last remnants of a once much wider spread of the Fremington till. Several of them are very similar in composition to the erratics found within the till at Fremington. If they do represent a lag deposit from this glaciation then their littoral location requires re-examination. It may simply be that the shore platform is the only site where the erratics are likely to be on view. Seawards, the ocean draws a curtain; landwards, they may be present, but are buried beneath head, having been soliflucted down from higher ground. Indeed, the only place that these blocks might have escaped solifluction and burial in the valleys or coastal spreads of head are on the near-flat hill-tops, hence perhaps the survival *in situ* of the isolated erratic on the crest of Baggy Point.

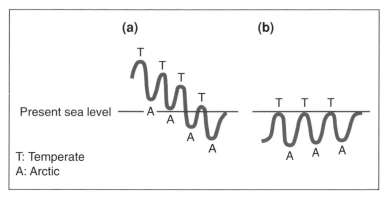

*Figure 13: Sea level change (a) staircase or (b) yo-yo?*

Locations and descriptions of the main erratics are shown in Figure 12a. The largest, approaching 50 tonnes, is a granulite gneiss somewhat similar in composition to rocks found in western Scotland. This coarse-grained altered granite boulder (Photo 11) is located at Freshwater Gut (SS 427400).

### Pleistocene shore platforms
The erratics lie on shore platforms higher than those being actively cut by modern seas, although some are washed by spring tides. These platforms are of unknown age. They pre-date the erratics and are presumed to relate to periods of high interglacial sea levels.

At Saunton (SS 437379) a platform at 5m OD is well-developed. The giant erratic at Freshwater Gut rests on a platform at 7.5m OD. At Pencil Rock (SS 423402) a higher platform, at 13.7m OD, notches the sloping cliff. It is not suggested that these heights accurately indicate specific high sea level still-stands; the platforms vary considerably in height, sloping both towards the sea and alongshore. Because of their discontinuous nature and the fact that in some places they grade one into another and in others are inter-cliffed, it is also not possible to be sure just how many stages of shore cutting the platforms represent. Where shoreline processes have etched out weaknesses in the steeply dipping Devonian Beds, these ancient rock platforms still exhibit differential erosion. Straight gullies emphasise the direction of joints, bedding planes and faults.

### Pleistocene raised beaches
The 12-tonne pink gneissose granite erratic at Saunton (SS 437379) is partly sealed in by overlying raised beach material, which in turn is overlain by thick deposits of head. Thus field evidence from quite a small area provides the basis for an outline sequence of coastal events, even if absolute dates are missing.

At Saunton the raised beach material seems to have amassed against the cliffs in much the same way as modern beach deposits are accumulating at the rear of Morte Bay. These Pleistocene sands flank

*Photo 11: The 50-tonne giant erratic* at Freshwater Gut, Croyde Bay (SS 427400)
Photo: Peter Keene

Saunton Down, exceptionally reaching a height of 76m OD
(SS 434382). The deposit varies considerably in thickness but locally
exceeds 30m. Shell fragments within the sands have provided the
calcium carbonate which in places has cemented the sand into a hard
'sandrock'. Within this sandrock are pipes of unconsolidated, non-
calcareous sand, perhaps representing preferential drainage routes for
some more acidic surface water. Some of these pipes attain a width of
over one metre (SS 438378) (Figure 12a, number 12).

   Because of its location and the presence of large dune-bedded
structures, the main upper part of this raised beach is thought to be
fossil coastal sand-dunes, analogous to the present dunes of Braunton
Burrows. The presence of fossil land snails identical to those living on
Braunton Burrows indicate that the climate was similar to today's.
However, in places (SS 432382), the upper part of the dune deposits
show signs of disturbance and heaving by the penetration of frost-
action into the subsoil, typical of an arctic or periglacial environment.
Presumably, the climate deteriorated after the dunes were formed.

There is less agreement on the environment of deposition of the lower part of this raised beach. Pebble and shingle beds, some cemented to the rock platform, clearly suggest a wave-washed deposit. There are even barnacles in their original growth positions, still attached to the Pleistocene rocky shore platform (SS 439378), (Figure 12a, number 12). However, between this beach and the aeolian deposits are up to 3m of cemented sands which lack the structure of the large dunes. Could this be part of the sandy shore which nurtured the development of the dune complex in the same way that Saunton Sands support Braunton Burrows today? Fossil **flute structures** in the sands (SS 445377) show on-shore wind directions similar to those of today. What is more, these sands contain marine shells such as periwinkles, limpets, oysters and mussels. However, this is not conclusive proof; walk the backshore and fore-dunes of Braunton Burrows and you can find the same selection of debris whipped up from Saunton Sands by onshore winds.

The lower sandrock sequence remains open to several interpretations, but standing on the beach at Croyde you may look at the cliffs and speculate on a sequence of events where coarse shoreline deposits of interbedded shingle, sand and pebbles pass up through backshore and low fore-dune deposits, which are in turn eventually overcome by progressing large mobile dunes.

A contrasting site is that of Pencil Rock (SS 423402). Here, the raised beach rests on a shore platform cut across steeply inclined slates. The base of the beach at 13.7m OD is composed of 1-2m of well-rounded pebbles and shingle set within a background of coarse sand and marine shell fragments. This is clearly shore material, but there are blocks of angular sandstone and shale which suggest that its location beneath cliffs provided the beach with numerous cliff fragments. These fragments continue upwards into 3m of cemented sands. There is general agreement that these are wave-washed sands and that the 4m of sandrock above this are dune-bedded aeolian deposits. These deposits cling to the steeply shelving seawards slope, and looking towards Croyde, can be followed by eye along the shore. Notice how the tilted detached blocks of sandrock are gradually sliding towards the sea. Pencil Rock is a good vantage point from which to view the several levels of shore platform visible in this area, and the apron of head which masks the back slopes of Croyde Bay.

## Ordering and dating events

The coastal apron of head has been discussed in relation to Westward Ho! and the coombes of the Hartland peninsula. It brings us towards the present day, for these deposits grade conformably upwards into the fine-grained hill-wash of subsoil which is subject to the slope processes of our present interglacial, temperate climate.

Thus, in this small area, we find exposed a series of deposits, each relating to a recognisable climatic environment. This should enable us to reconstruct some of the Quaternary events that have so dramatically influenced the coastline. It is relatively easy to assign either 'Arctic' or 'Temperate' labels to each of these deposits:

| | |
|---|---|
| Hill-wash | Temperate |
| Head | Arctic |
| Sandrock and raised beach | Temperate |
| Erratics | Arctic |
| Shore platforms | Temperate? |

Next, working back from the present, these can be assigned to specific Quaternary stages. This interpretation, Alternative 1 in Table 2, is widely supported.

## Table 2: Summary of alternative interpretations of Quaternary events in North Devon

| Stage<br>t = temperate<br>(Interglacial)<br>a = arctic<br>(Glacial) | Alternative 1 | Alternative 2 | Alternative 3 |
|---|---|---|---|
| | These alternatives are not mutually exclusive | | |
| **HOLOCENE**<br>(Flandrian)<br>(Postglacial)<br>(t)<br>10 000 BP | Westward Ho! Pebble Ridge, clay and peat beds<br>Braunton Burrows, Northam Burrows, estuary infilling<br>Renewal of marine cliff cutting<br>Rise in sea level (Flandrian Transgression) drowned<br>lower river valleys creating estuaries and rias | | |
| **DEVENSIAN**<br>(a)<br><br>90 000 BP | Low sea-level (-110m)<br>Old cliffs degraded<br>All Head deposited<br>forming coastal aprons<br>and coombe infills | Low sea-level(-110m)<br>'Upper' Head deposited and<br>disturbed by periglacial<br>processes | |
| **IPSWICHIAN**<br>(t)<br><br>130 000 BP | High sea-level (+8m)<br>All raised beaches formed<br>including Penhill Pt,<br>Croyde, Saunton, Lee<br>Bay, Westward Ho!<br>Dismemberment of<br>Valley of Rocks by sea<br>Coastal cliffs cut | High sea-level (+8m)<br>Low tide pebble beds at<br>Westward Ho! (beneath<br>outer clay banks)<br>Possible weathering and<br>erosion horizons between<br>Upper and Lower head | |
| Older stages<br>in the<br>Pleistocene | (a) cold stage<br>Ice cap reached N Devon<br>Fremington Till<br>(Anglian glacial stage?)<br>(450 000 BP)<br>Coastal erratics deposited<br>as part of same ice<br>advance or rafted to shore<br>by icebergs during<br>higher sea-level episode. | (a) cold stage<br>Ice cap reached N Devon<br>Fremington Till<br>Croyde 'weathered till'<br>Lower Head deposited<br>(main solifluction infill)<br>(t) warm stage<br>All raised beaches above<br>OD formed<br>(a) cold stage Coastal erratics<br>ice-rafted to shore | |
| Early<br>Pleistocene<br>Late Tertiary | Shore platforms cut<br>Coastal plateaux develop | Shore platforms cut<br>Coastal plateaux develop | |

However, one danger of 'counting from the top' is that if evidence of events is missing then the count goes wrong. For example, what if the head is the product of two cold stages rather than one, the intervening temperate stage simply not producing any deposits? We have already noted that at Westward Ho! there are two distinct layers of head above the raised beach. A section of head well worth looking at, with this in mind, is found in the cliff opposite Middleborough House, Croyde (SS 428398). Here, where the path cuts diagonally across the cliff to reach the beach below, two levels of head-like material are clearly visible. Sealed-in, ice-distorted features below a possible weathering horizon have been used to suggest that the head deposit here represents two distinct cold stages separated by warmer conditions. If this is indeed the case then the calendar of Quaternary events has to be reconsidered. Alternative 2 in Table 2 represents one way in which an extended timescale may be viewed.

The inconclusive nature of the debate may give rise to frustration; alternatively there may be rejoicing that so much remains to be discovered. As the memoir accompanying the geology map of the district puts it, 'the field is wide open to speculation and theory, unencumbered by too rigid a framework of fact'. Alternative 3 in Table 2 is left blank for such speculation.

Central to many of these problems is the fact that in North Devon no Quaternary deposits older than the Holocene have been firmly dated. Limpet shells from the raised beach at Saunton, dated by a technique known as 'amino acid racemisation', hint at shells in two distinct age groups. This can be interpreted as a double sea-level peak during the Ipswichian, an Ipswichian beach containing older reworked shells, or the presence of an older beach. Recent radioisotopic work, thermoluminescence, implies that the sands are Ipswichian. Uncertainties inherent in relatively new techniques leave all these interpretations equivocal.

Access
There are spectacular views of Braunton Burrows and Bideford Bay from laybys on the B3231 on Saunton Down (SS 438381), but to view the Saunton Down exposures discussed here the large car park immediately behind the beach at Saunton Sands (SS 446377) is the best starting point. From here a foreshore walk will take you to sites 12 to 9 shown in Figure 12a.

A good starting point for the Baggy Point sections is the National Trust car park near Middleborough (SS 432397). Coaches must park earlier – at Croyde Beach (SS 436395). At Middleborough (site 6), a path leads to the foreshore which can be followed around to Freshwater Gut (site 5). Shortly after this, the clifftop pathway can be regained by a steep cliff-slope scramble (in 1996). This is not difficult but care should be exercised at all these cliff-side locations, particulary where steeply dipping beds plunge straight to the sea. Pencil Rock (site 4), requires a slight detour. A small track leads down from the main cliff path at a point marked by a small raised inspection cover on a cement base.

# EXMOOR: VALLEY OF ROCKS

The style of the Exmoor coast (Photo 12) contrasts markedly with that south of Hartland Point (Photos 1 and 2). Flat-topped cliffs with discordant seaward-jumping reefs are replaced by classic 'hog's-back' cliffs developed on the scarp edge of inland-dipping rocks, the strike of which runs nearly parallel to the coast. Although less precipitous than the Atlantic-facing Hartland cliffs, the Exmoor coast presents a high, almost continuous rampart to the Bristol Channel, and is probably fault-controlled. The seaward facing scarp slope of the Great Hangman, composed of resistant Hangman Grits, reaches a height of 318m (SS 602482).

Only the lowest section of these cliffs is the product of modern marine processes. Above this steep fresh-faced wall, there are vegetated convex slopes that are the result of structural control, current slope processes and past periglacial activity. The relict periglacial forms include low-angled rock benches (altiplanation terraces) thought to be the product of a variety of cold environment processes. These can be identified on Trentishoe Down (SS 628479) and Holdstone Down (SS 620479) where periglacial patterned ground is visible.

The hog's-backed cliff rampart is breached by a series of deep coombes. The Heddon valley (SS 655493) enters the sea at right angles, its straight valley flanked by steep, partially vegetated rock slopes at angles of up to 43°. These slopes were formed by accelerated frost-action during past episodes of periglaciation. Caddow Combe

© *Crown Copyright*

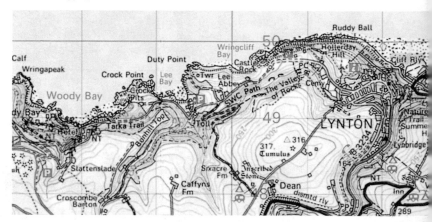

(SS 756507), immediately east of the Foreland Point, is also flanked by fine runs of partially vegetated screes. Both these coombes are cut in the coarse sandstones of the Hangman Grits. Other valleys run near-parallel to the coast. At Ilfracombe (SS 520478) and Watermouth (SS 552485) the lower courses of the valleys have been drowned and exhibit incipient dissection by the sea. The most spectacular and well-known of these coastal valleys is the Valley of Rocks (SS 707497).

The Valley of Rocks is a dry, streamless coombe running parallel to the sea yet separated from it by a ridge of well-jointed fine-grained sandstones, part of the Lynton Slates. Local near-horizontal bedding has encouraged the formation of a series of spectacular castellated crestal peaks. Figure 14 suggests that the Valley of Rocks is another example of a sea-captured valley. When only fragments of an ancient river system have been preserved, one way of testing a former connection would be to see if surviving remnants fit into a smooth long profile. Simpson in 1953 demonstrated that the upper tributaries of the East Lyn, the Valley of Rocks, the Lee Abbey valley and a further fragment at Crock Point, could all be joined by a curved long profile which might represent the former valley floor. Irregularities in

*Photo 12: The 'hog's-back' rampart of the north Exmoor coast, looking east from above the Little Hangman (SS 585481). In the mid-distance is the Great Hangman, in the far distance is Heddon's Mouth (SS 655498) and beyond that Highveer Point (SS 656499). Photo: Aerofilms Ltd*

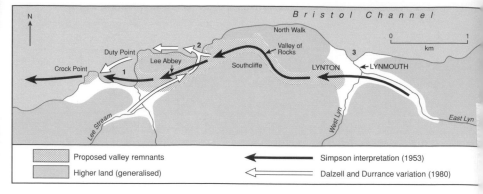

**Figure 14:** *Interpretations of the evolution of the Valley of Rocks*

this long profile were explained as subsequent landform modifications as the valley was gradually dismembered by coastal erosion, first at Lee Bay (1), then at Wringcliff Bay (2) and finally at Lynmouth itself (3), leaving the whole of the Valley of Rocks dry (Figure 14).

Unlike the Milford Water (SS 224235) examined previously, the floor of the Valley of Rocks is deeply buried in head deposits, over 30m deep in places. This casts doubt on the accuracy of the profile proposed by Simpson because it was surveyed along the surface of the valley floor. A later survey by Dalzell and Durrance (1980) used electrical resistance meters to plot the depth of head and locate the buried floor of solid rock. The results (Figure 15a) suggested to them that the Valley of Rocks (East Lyn) stream could not have continued over the higher rock col of Lee Abbey. They therefore favoured a route out through Wringcliff Bay, with the Lee valley as an east flowing tributary, the alternative shown in Figure 14.

Unconsolidated deposits at Lee Bay (Figure 15b) can be reasonably interpreted as indicating that the most recent date at which sea-capture at this point could have occurred was about 100 000 years ago (Ipswichian).

The dry Valley of Rocks has undergone considerable modification since it was beheaded. These modifications are principally related to periglacial processes active in the subsequent Devensian cold stage.

Frost attack, by promoting the active retreat of the walls of the valley, must have played a considerable part in widening the valley and fostering the destruction of its seaward wall. Solifluction stripped weathered material from the valley sides exposing sounder rock as tors of well-jointed sandstone, and infilling the valley floor with head. On the seaward side of the valley the crestal turrets of rock are flanked by screes of debris released from these frost-riven peaks. To the south, valley-side tors relating to ribs of more massive bedrock protrude through the head (SS 704496). Downslope, trails of blocks rafted away by solifluction demonstrate the partial destruction of these tors by frost attack.

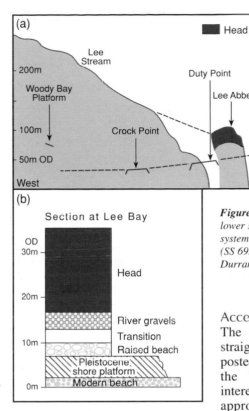

**Figure 15:** *(a) the long profile of the lower section of the Valley of Rocks system (b) a cliff section at Lee Bay (SS 693493). Based on Dalzell and Durrance, 1980*

## Access

The access from Lynton is straightforward and well signposted. There is a car park in the Valley of Rocks. An interesting alternative route to approach the sequence of features is via Martinhoe Common (SS 674485). An old coach route runs from here to the Valley of Rocks. The road is suitable for cars but *not* coaches. A coastal walk which might be integrated into an approach to the Valley of Rocks from the west is that which runs from Hunter's Inn (SS 655482) to Woody Bay (SS 673489), where the road can be joined. From Hunter's Inn, follow the track which climbs across the eastern side of the Heddon Valley (SS 656488) which forms part of the Somerset and Devon Coast Path. Across the valley, scree slopes and their vegetational succession are well demonstrated. The path from above Highveer Point (SS 658495) to Woody Bay (SS 673489) affords magnificent coastal views towards the Valley of Rocks. This walk takes in the essential characteristics of Exmoor's coastal scenery.

There are spectacular views of Lynmouth and the Lyn valleys from Summerhouse Hill (SS 726490) and from Hollerday Hill (SS 715498). If you doubt the power of the Lyn to incise itself to sea level, consider the flood of 15 August 1952, when an estimated 100 000 tonnes of boulders moved through the village. The river mouth boulder delta also bears testimony to the vigour of this stream when in spate; a reminder that low-frequency, high-intensity events are very important in the modification of coasts. On a human scale the North Devon cliffs look misleadingly timeless.

# GLOSSARY

**BP** Years before the present (e.g. MYBP: million years BP).

**Erratic** A stone, distinctive in that its parent rock outcrop is not local. Here it is used to describe far-travelled ice-transported boulders.

**Fetch** The distance of open water over which winds can freely generate surface waves.

**Flute structures** Here used to describe elongated hollows resulting from the scouring action of winds over sand, sometimes preserved and indicating ancient wind directions.

**Frost-action** Repeated freezing and thawing of trapped water causing rock shattering and heaving and downslope displacement of debris by gravity.

**Head** Originally a local farming term for deep rubbly subsoil, it is now used to describe the mantle of unconsolidated material produced, in part, by frost shattering and transported downslope by solifluction.

**Lag deposit** The coarsest material (e.g. boulders) left behind when the finer materials of a deposit have been removed by wind, wave or stream.

**Neogene** The geological period which started with the Miocene 23 MYBP.

**Periglacial** Literally peripheral to ice masses. Used to describe very cold arctic-like environments where freeze-thaw rock-shattering and solifluction are important processes.

**Pleistocene** The geological period covering most of the last two million years (see Table 2 page 40 for details).

**Ria** A valley partly drowned by a rise in sea level. Unlike an estuary, it is characterised by relatively steep valley sides.

**Raised beach** Beach deposits found in a position above present sea level. It may or may not be the same age as the shore platform upon which these beaches commonly rest.

**Shore platform** A platform close to sea level usually cut by a variety of marine processes. Sometimes termed a wave-cut platform.

**Solifluction** The slow flow-like movement of material downslope when soil is saturated by water. Particularly active in periglacial environments where spring thaw melts ice within the soil, and deeper, permanently frozen, subsoils inhibit free drainage. Frost-action also liberates debris.

**Till** The unsorted deposit which is the result of transportation of material by ice. A landform composed mainly of till may be described as a moraine.

**Wave-period** The time taken for two successive wave crests (a wavelength) to pass a fixed point.

**Variscan orogeny** An episode of earth movements, including heavy folding and faulting, culminating in Late Carboniferous times. It is also known as the Armorican or Hercynian Orogeny.

# BIBLIOGRAPHY

Arber, E.A.N. (1911) *The coast scenery of North Devon*. Dent, London. (Facsimile edition 1969, Kingsmead Reprints, Bath.)

Arber, M.A. (1974) 'The cliffs of North Devon' in *Proceedings of the Geological Association*, 85 (2), 147-157.

Balaam, N.D., Levitan, B. & Straker, V. (eds) (1987) 'Prehistoric and Romano-British sites at Westward Ho! Devon: archaeological and palaeo-environmental survey 1983-4' in *Studies in palaeoeconomy and environment in South West England*, BAR Series 181, 163-264.

Dalzell, D. & Durrance, E.M. (1980) 'The evolution of the Valley of Rocks' in *Transactions of the Institute of British Geographers*, 5(1), 66-79.

De Freitas, M.H. (1972) 'Some examples of cliff failure in SW England' in *Proceedings of the Ussher Society*, 2, 388-97.

Durrance, E.M. & Laming, D.J.C. (eds) (1982) *The geology of Devon*. University of Exeter.

Edmunds, E.A., Williams, B.J. & Taylor, R.T. (1979) 'Geology of Bideford and Lundy Island' in *Memoirs of the Geological Survey of Great Britain*. London.

Edmonds, E.A., Whittaker, A. & Williams, B.J. (1985) 'Geology of the country around Ilfracombe and Barnstaple' in *Memoirs of the Geological Survey of Great Britain*. London.

Freshney, E.C., Edmunds, E.A., Taylor, R.T. & Williams, B.J. (1979) 'Geology of the country around Bude and Bradworthy' in *Memoirs of the Geological Survey of Great Britain*. London.

Keene, P. (1992) *Coastal management and coastal erosion at Westward Ho!*. Thematic Trails, Oxford.

Kidson, C. (1977) 'The coast of South West England' in Kidson, C. & Tooley, M.J. (eds) *The Quaternary History of the Irish Sea*. Seel House Press, Liverpool.

Madgett, Paul A. & Inglis, A.B. (1987) 'A re-appraisal of the erratic suite of the Saunton and Croyde Areas, North Devon' in *Transactions of the Devonshire Association*, 119, 135-44.

Simpson, S. (1953) 'The development of the Lyn drainage system and its relation to the origin of the coast between Combe Martin and Porlock' in *Proceedings of the Geological Association*, 64, 14-23.

Stephens, N. (1970) 'The West Country' in Lewis, C. A. (ed) *The Glaciation of Wales and Adjoining Regions*. Longman, London, 267-314.

Willis, A.J., Folkes, B.F., Hope-Simpson, J.F. & Yemm, E.W. (1959) 'Braunton Burrows: the dune system and its vegetation' Parts I and II; Part I: *Journal of Ecology*, 47(1) 1-24; Part II: *Journal of Ecology*, 47(2) 249-88.

# Associated teaching aids
# from Thematic Trails

Each of the five areas covered by Classic Landforms of the North Devon Coast has a nesting set of thematic trails which provide a more detailed examination and interactive commentary on selected themes within each area. The trails serve as reference booklets, landscape companions and guided walks.

*Geology at Hartland Quay* Chris Cornford & Alan Childs

*The Cliffs of Hartland Quay* Peter Keene

*Strawberry Water to Marsland Mouth* Peter Keene

*The Cliffs of Westward Ho!* Peter Keene

*Westward Ho! Against the Sea* Peter Keene

*Coastal Management and Erosion at Westward Ho!* Peter Keene

*Northam Burrows: estuary environments* Janet & Peter Keene

*Braunton Burrows Ecology Trail* Janet Keene

*The Cliffs of Saunton* Peter Keene & Chris Cornford

*Lyn in Flood, Watersmeet to Lynmouth* Peter Keene & Derek Elsom

*Valley of Rocks, Lynton* Peter Keene & Brian Pearce

These trails are available direct from the educational publishing charity Thematic Trails, in both their original form and as expendable educational workbooks, without detailed commentary and with spaces for answers. Permission to copy workbook versions need not be sought providing the copies are not for resale. For more information or a catalogue please contact:

**Peter Keene (Editor), Thematic Trails, Geography Unit, Oxford Brookes University, Oxford OX3 0BP
Direct telephone: 01865 483753**

**Registered charity no 801188**